'S SCHOOL LIBR

"A wonderfully imaginative and stylish piece of work" Alan Moore, author of *Watchmen* and *V for Vendetta*

"Deliciously strange and wonderful" **Forbidden Planet**

"An extraordinary, sexy, obsessive, decadent thing of wonder" **New Statesman**

"A tactile and visual joy; an artefact that makes you happy just to hold it in your hands" **Guardian Review**

"If it doesn't become an instant cult classic then the goths of this world are losing their usually impeccable taste" **Sunday Herald**

"A hypnotically beautiful gothic fantasy" **Jefferson Hack, Dazed & Confused**

"Kicked my ass and made me believe in the beautiful darkness of the world again" **Harmony Korine**

"Original and compelling. There's a seamless relationship between the images and the text, and the characters linger in the mind" **Anthony Minghella**

"Rarely has a comic book felt so sensual; your eyes demand time to caress each swirling curl and line" **Metro**

"An extraordinary-looking Gothic graphic novel, with a plot to match" **Sunday Express**

"Delightfully intricate, trippy and surreal" **Financial Times**

"A beautiful-looking graphic novel... The artwork is gorgeous; intricate and stylised" **SFX Magazine**

"Sharp surprising storytelling and intense, imaginative illustration combine to create real magic" **Paul Gravett**

There are those who love the rum and unusual, the uncanny, the macabre. Perhaps they wish for thrilling horrors in their own seemingly mundane lives... But they should beware what they wish for.

Take Salem Brownstone, for instance. For many years he ran the Sit & Spin Laundromat and was content with his lot. The Laundromat was his own fiefdom, and the customers presented him with a never-ending cavalcade of variety. And yet, somewhere deep down Salem believed he was destined for greater things, stranger things. Then one day they came to him in the unlikely form of a simple telegram...

MECCOTEL INC

Telegram

NEW MECCO CITY, AZANIA
12.09 P.M. 31 OCTOBER

SALEM O. BROWNSTONE ESQUIRE
C/O SIT AND SPIN LAUNDROMAT, SINKO

I REGRET TO INFORM YOU OF THE DEATH OF YOUR FATHER
JEDEDIAH BROWNSTONE. YOU ARE URGED TO TAKE
IMMEDIATE POSSESSION OF HIS HOUSE AND THE
CONTENTS THEREIN - A CAR WILL BE SENT
TO DRIVE YOU THERE TONIGHT AT 9 P.M.
LOLA Q

The low rumble of thunder rolls through the cement canyons of New Mecco City...

But Salem is too lost in thought to notice his surroundings.

After all these years of wanting to know my father, now it's too late. I've lost him.

The taxi pulls up outside a towering mansion.

Nice house. What was he — an undertaker?

If he knew where I was all along, why didn't he contact me before?

Strange music fills the air, mingled with sudden cries of joy or alarm.

Huh?

As he clutches the key to his inheritance, Salem turns to see the colourful shantytown of a circus encampment.

Hmm ... note to self: run away with the circus.

Well, here goes nothing...

The key catches momentarily and Salem is almost relieved. Then the door opens with a nerve-shattering creak.

Salem gropes for the switch, then light floods the room revealing...

A wand and a cape! What kind of a man was my father?

I knew he was in show business, but never imagined...

He was a magic man!

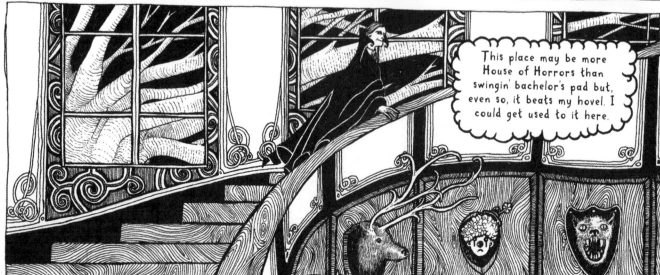

This place may be more House of Horrors than swingin' bachelor's pad but, even so, it beats my hovel. I could get used to it here.

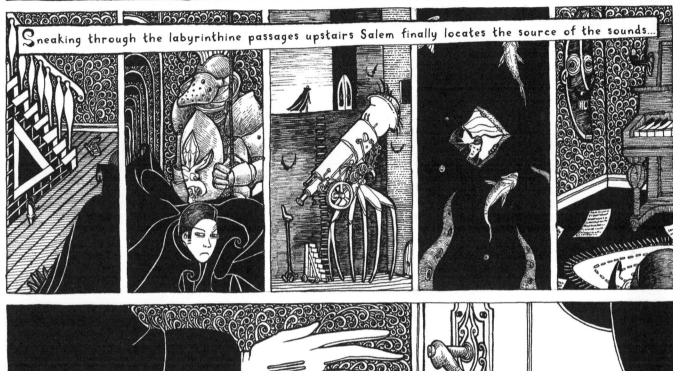

But this nocturnal thief is much more than just a common thug.

For a moment, they are both stunned into silence.

Then Salem finds his tongue...

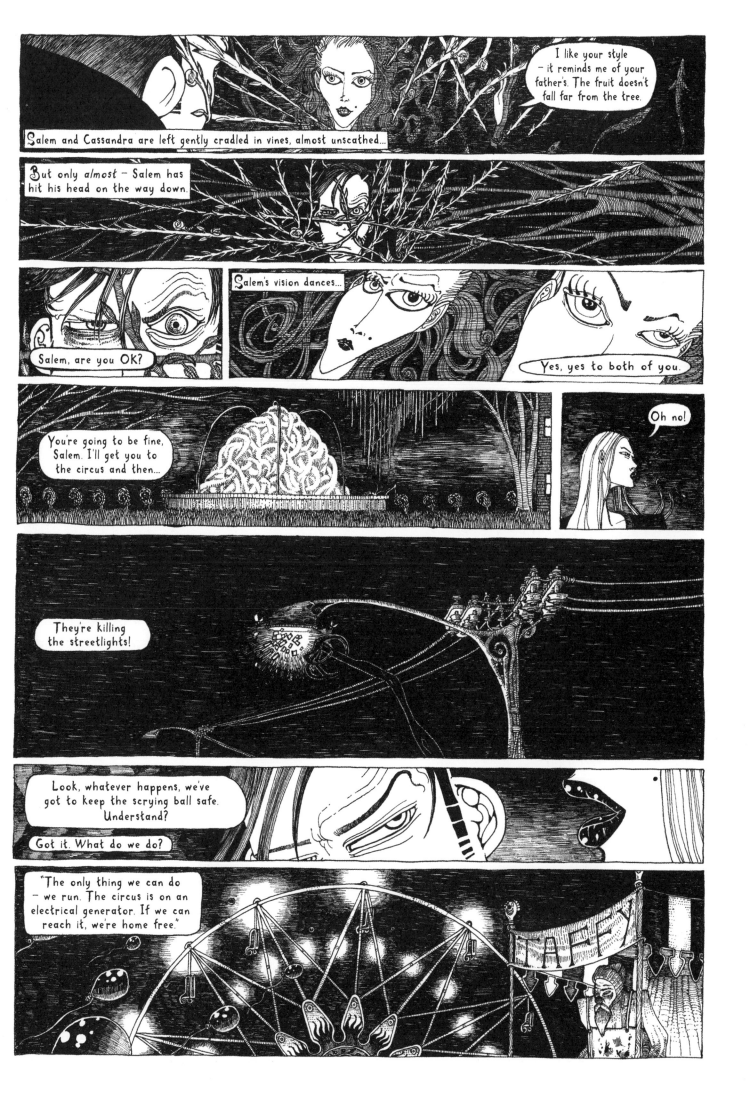

His mind bucks, then is free of its physical confines: a mote in the eye of God.

Salem is aware of his body, his name, his life, drifting somewhere far below. A sudden contraction of fear threatens to overwhelm him...

Then he is aware that he is not alone, and is comforted.

The smell of popcorn, sawdust and burned candyfloss can only mean...

THE CIRCUS!

Here, all that is ordinary is useless. Only the extraordinary survive...

ALLEYN'S SCHOOL LIBRARY

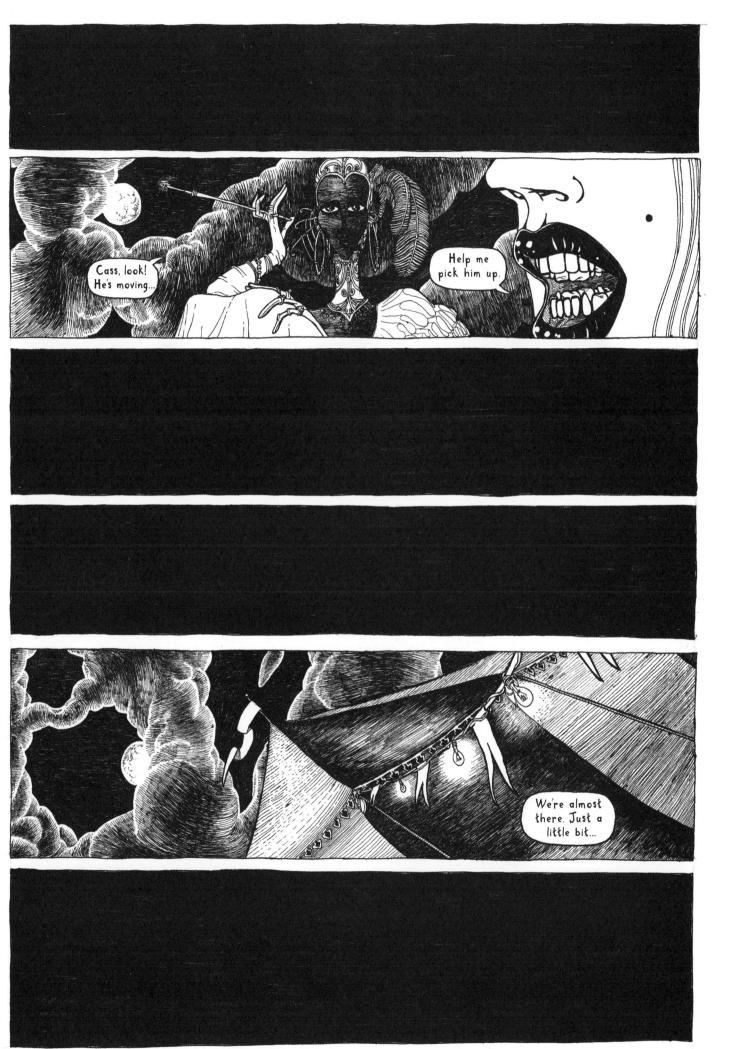

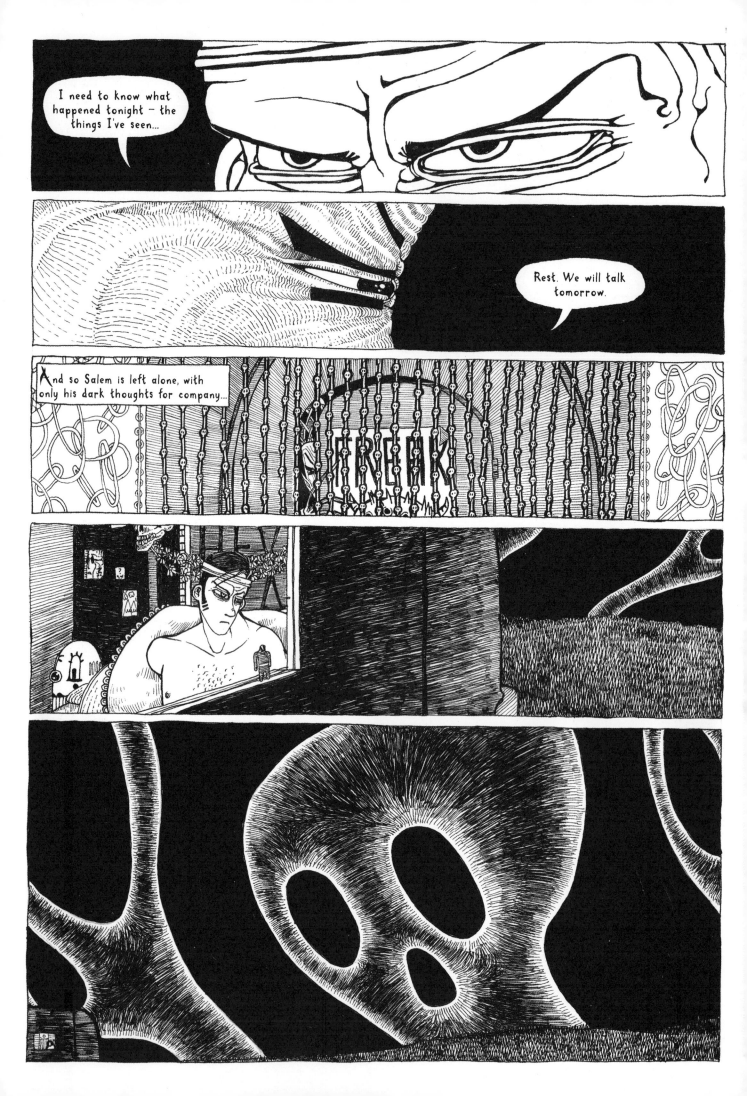

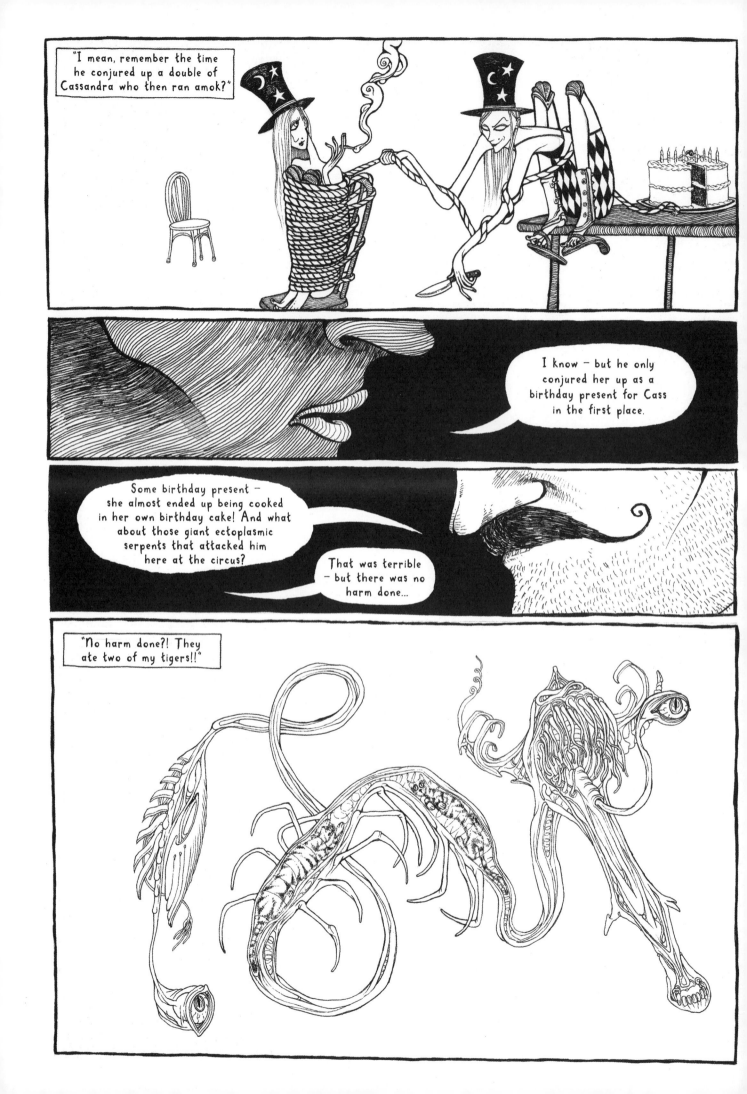

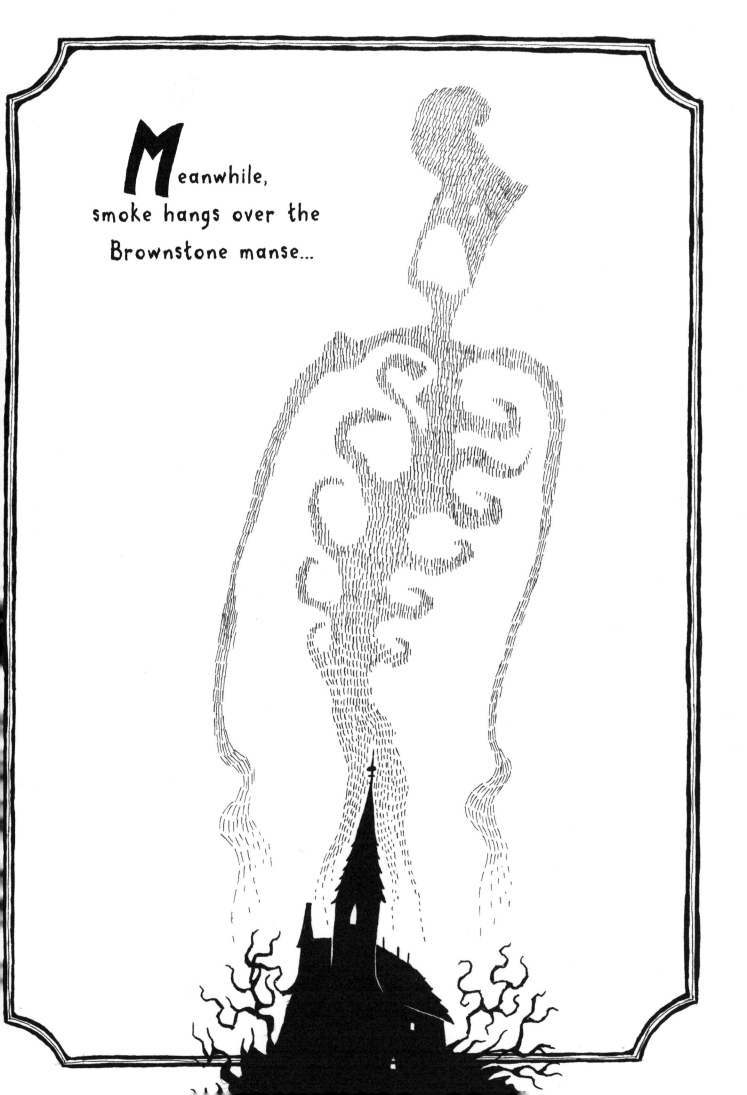

Meanwhile, smoke hangs over the Brownstone manse...

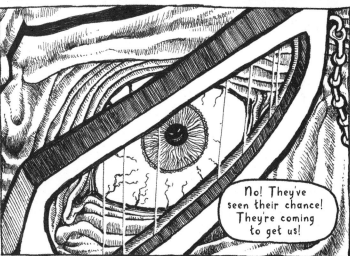

Lola Q's snake-like gaze is unwavering...

Her hand returns again and again to the dossier at her side.

Hey there, pretty lady, we're going downtown.

Suddenly...

I'm off duty.

She says she's off duty — can you believe that?!

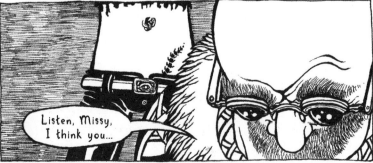

Listen, Missy, I think you...

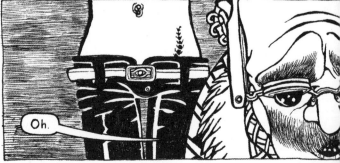

Oh.

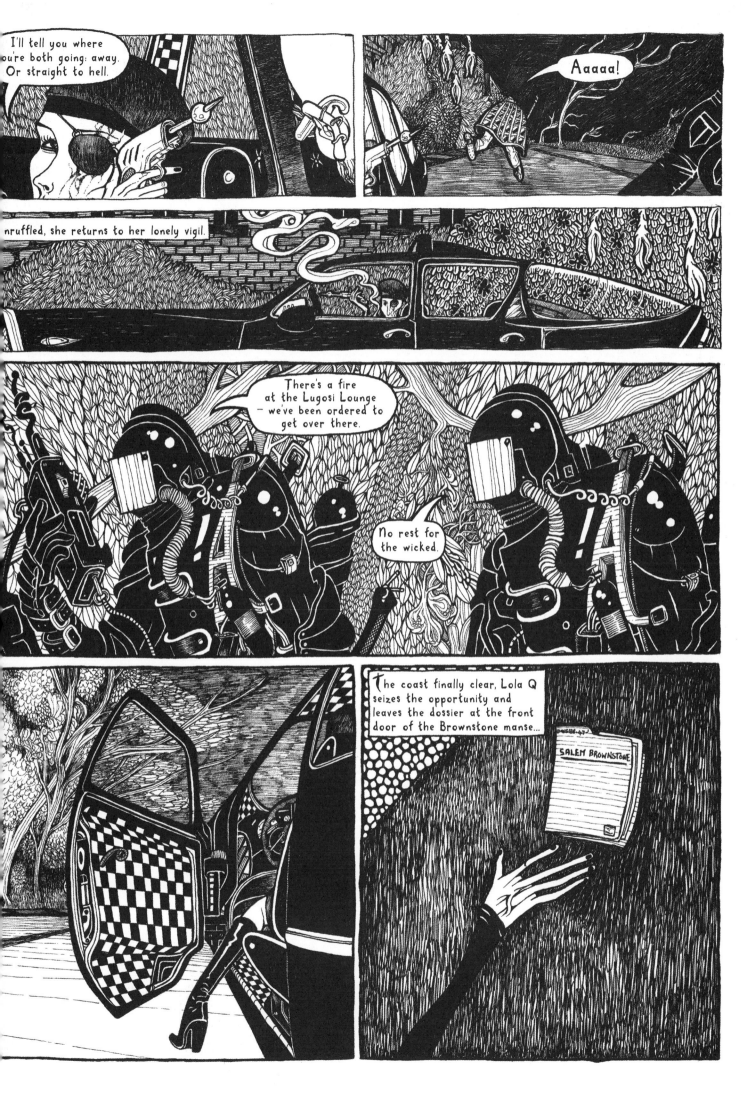

You ready to give me some answers?

I'll tell you all I know, although I fear that I'll create more questions than answers.

The first and most important fact is that your father was a good man. He spoke of you often, and of your achievements.

What did he know of my achievements? I haven't seen him since I was six years old!

"But he saw you. You winning the national tap dance championship."

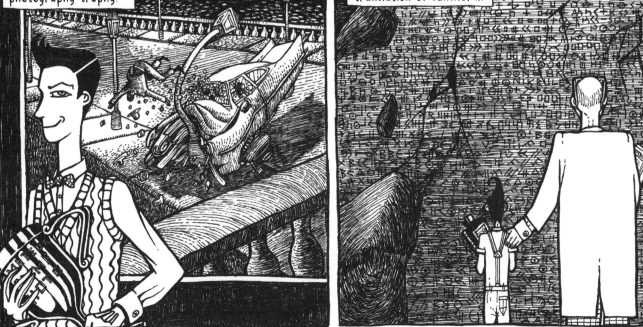

"The amateur crime photography trophy."

"Excellence in the translation of cuneiform."

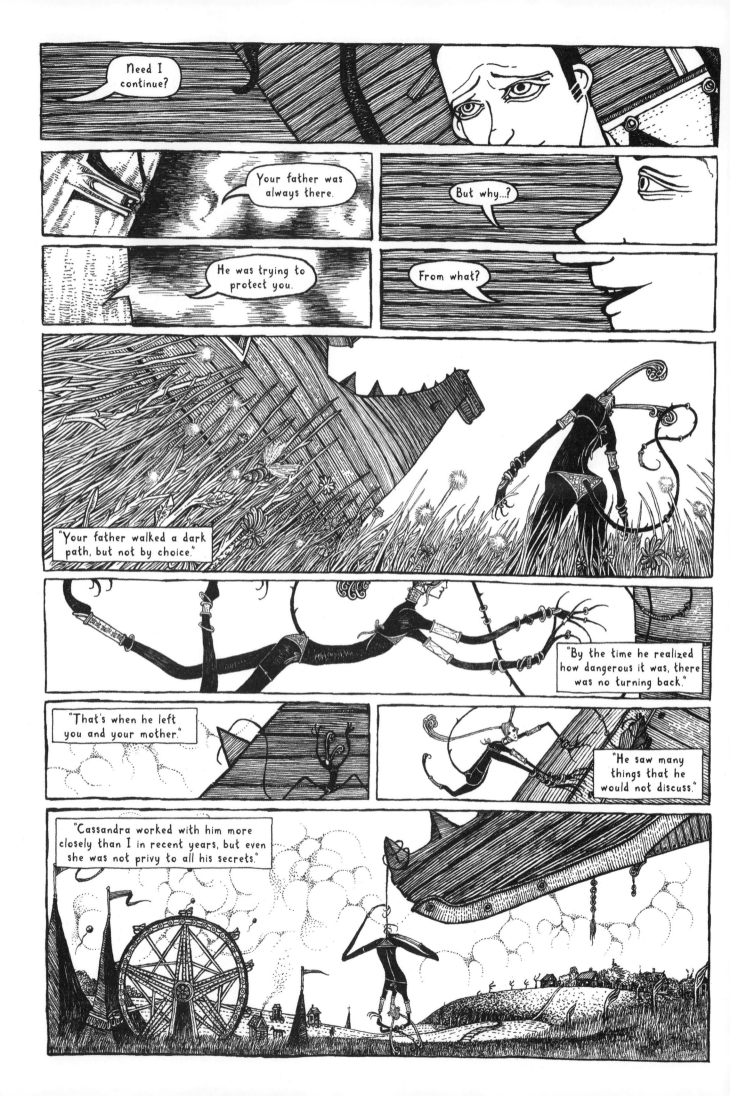

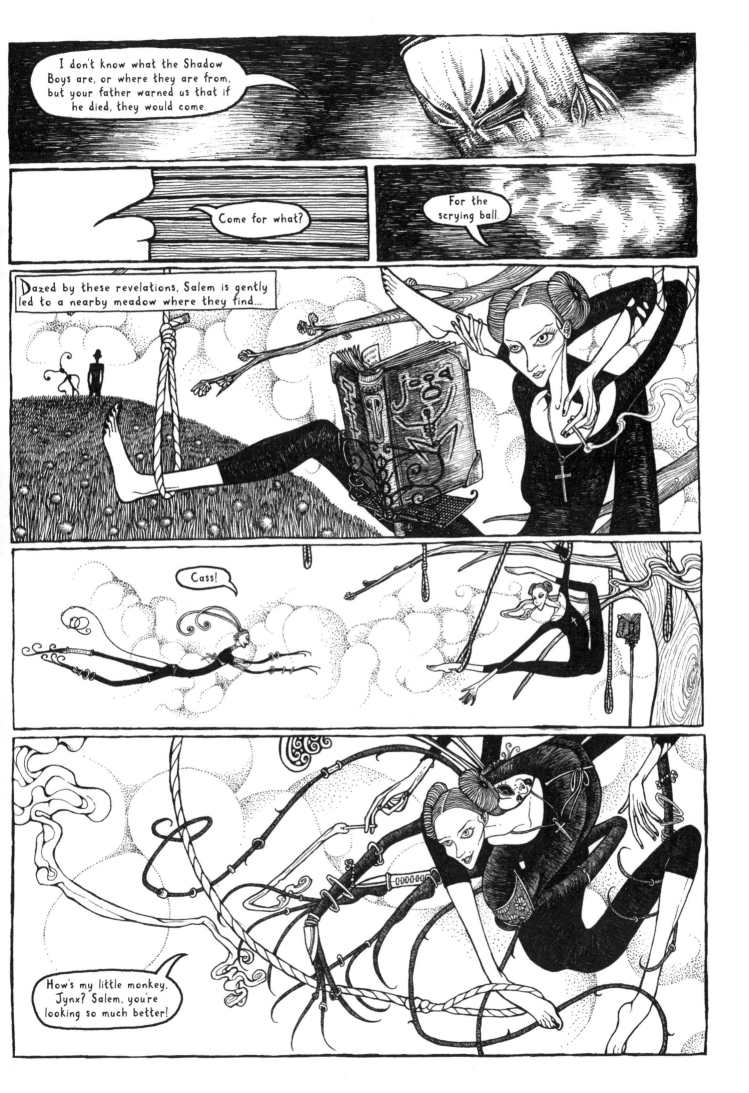

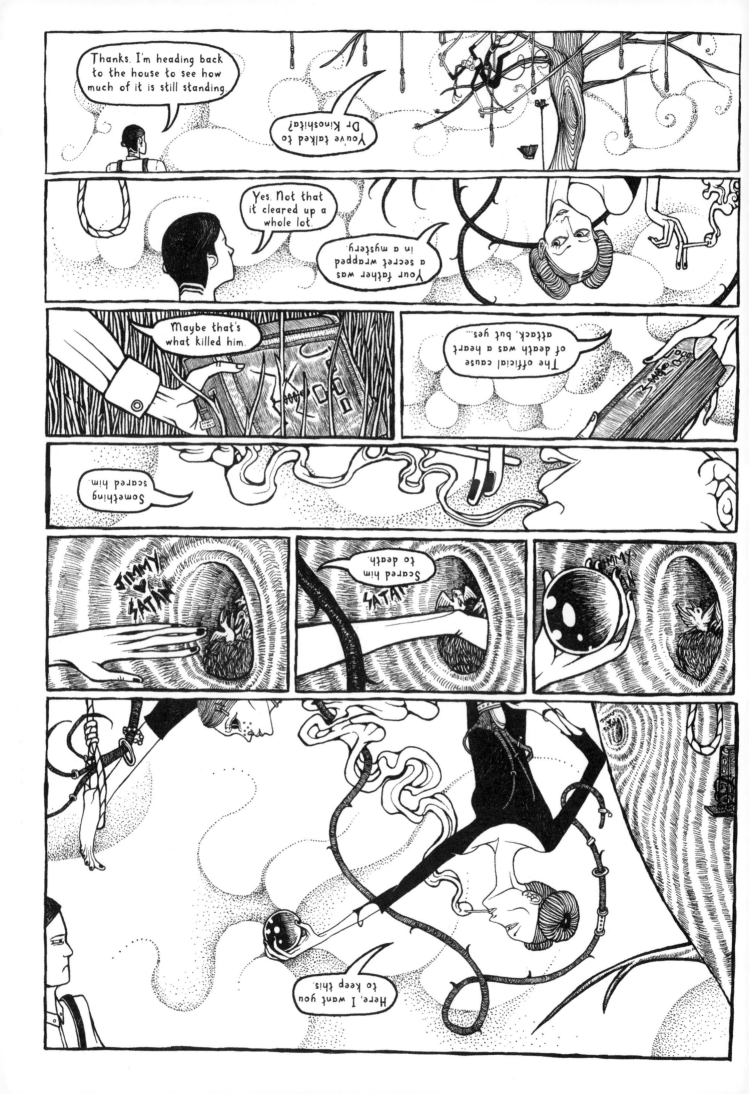

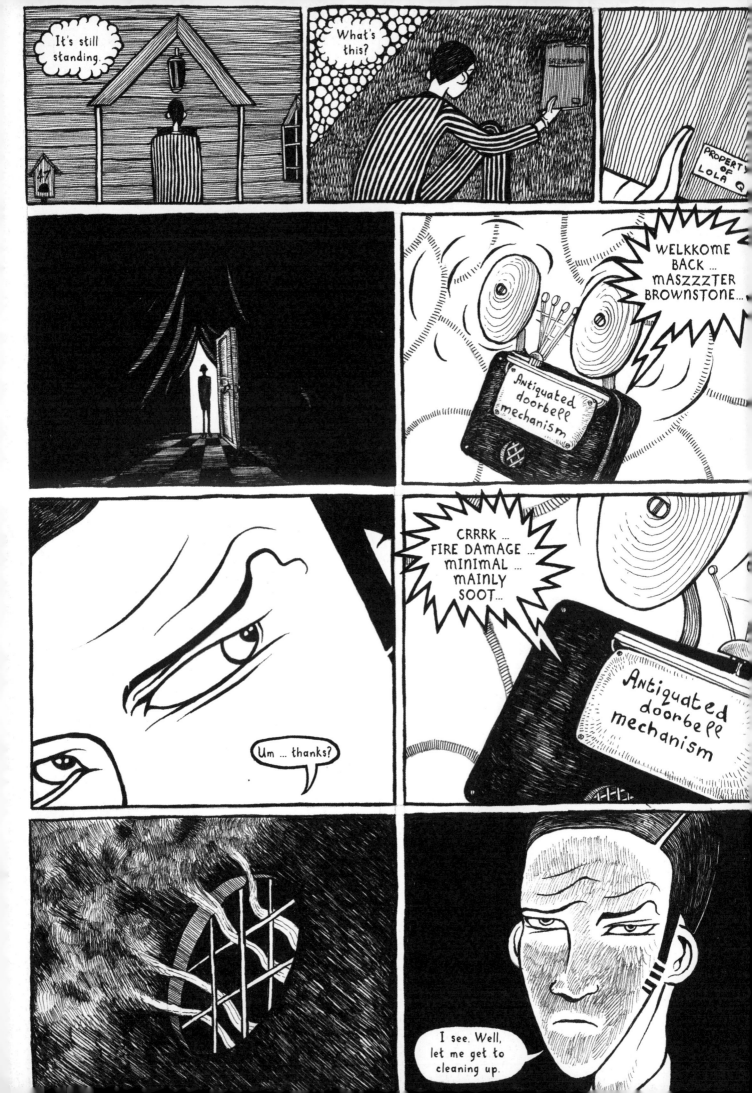

In another place...

...lies Mu' bric,
the Midnight City...

Further away than you can imagine, it is also closer than you think...

This vast megalopolis stands in a frozen desert that stretches off into forever...

Here it is always silent, always dark...

The citizens of this infernal city are covered in a fine ash of unimaginable cosmic despair...

They have only one purpose...

To serve the Dark Elders of Mu'bric.

THIS IS NO LONGER A SIMPLE MISSION TO OBTAIN THE ORB — WE WILL HAVE TO FIGHT FOR IT NEXT TIME.
NEXT TIME? ARE YOU FORGETTING WE DO NOT HAVE THE POWER TO SEND ANY MORE OF OUR KIND ACROSS THE VOID TO THEIR WORLD?
YOU ALWAYS DID DISPLAY A LAMENTABLE LACK OF IMAGAINATION.
HOW DARE...
TRUE, WE CANNOT CROSS OVER CORPOREALLY...
"...BUT THAT DOES NOT PRECLUDE OTHER OPTIONS..."

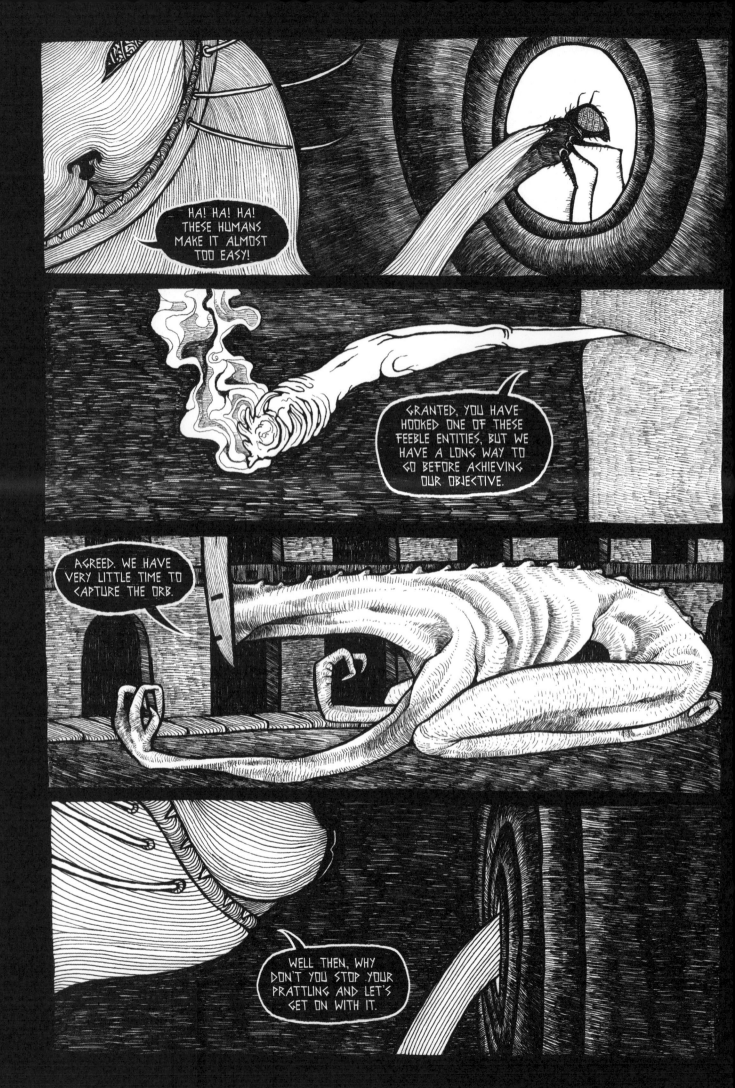

Not far from the circus lies an inky pond...

THERE'S ONE NOW...

Yes, I see it.

Moonlight illuminates the ghostly form of a swan gliding through the water with an arrogant elegance born of knowing no predator...

That is about to change...

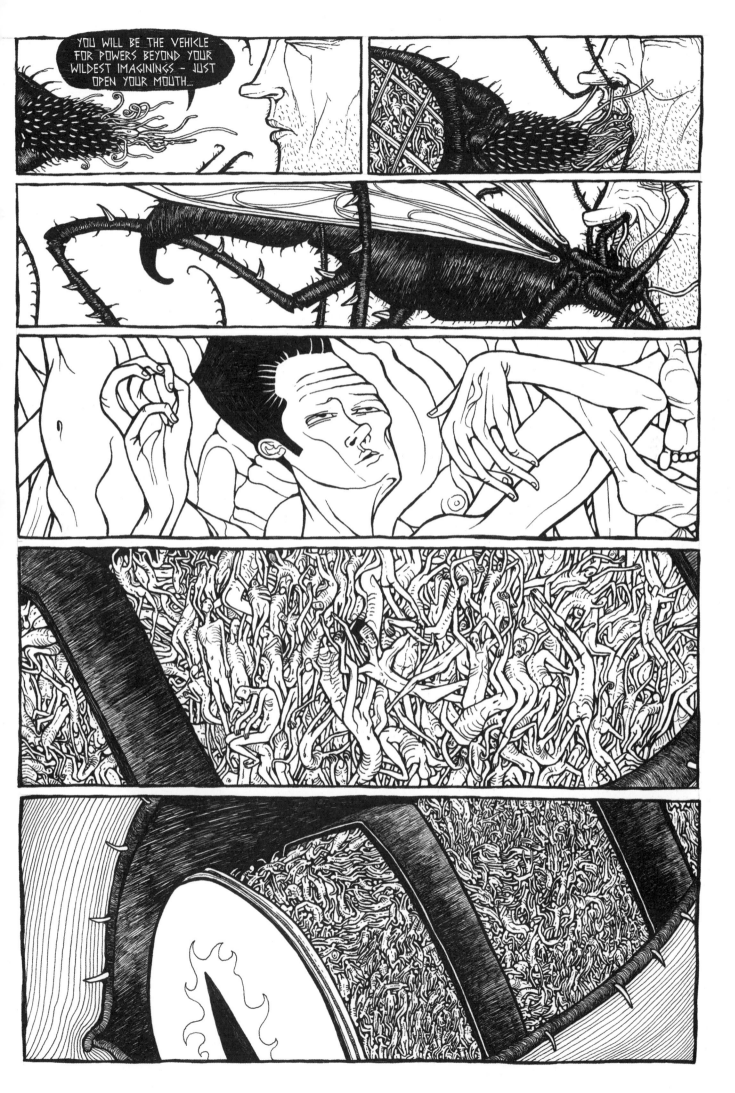

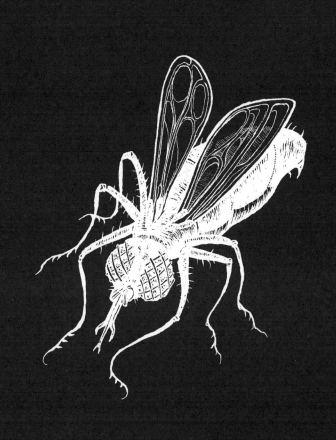

On the New Mecco City waterfront...

...in an apartment like so many others surrounding it...

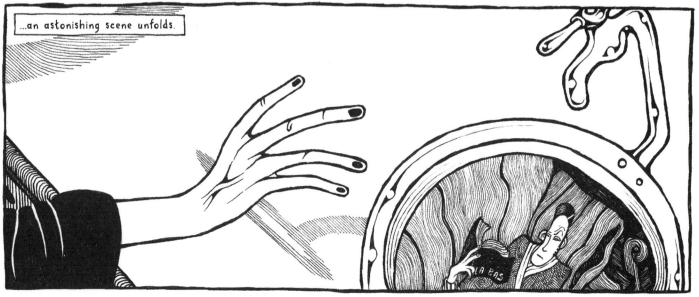

...an astonishing scene unfolds.

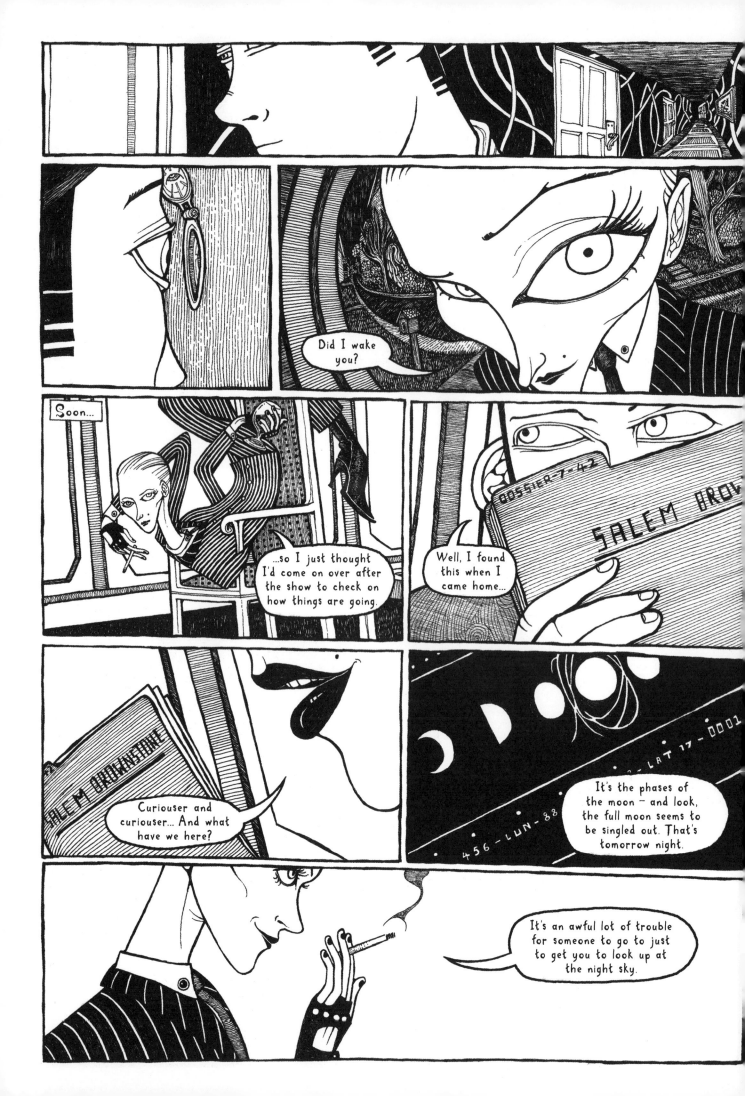

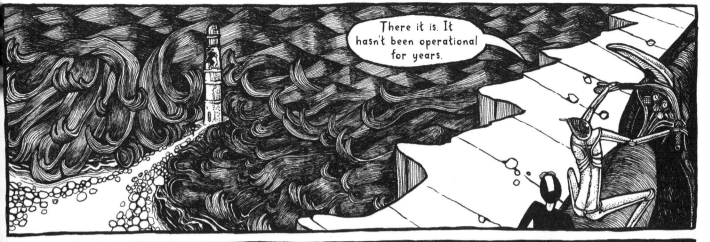

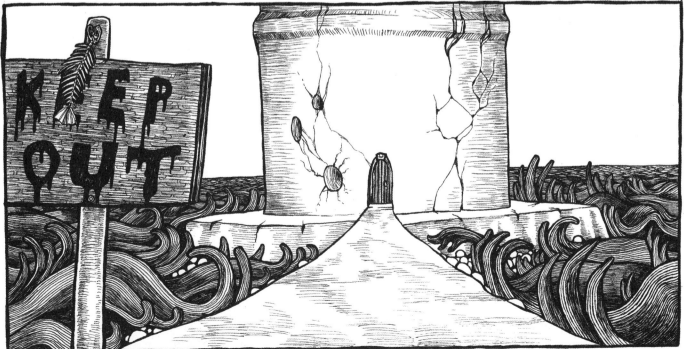

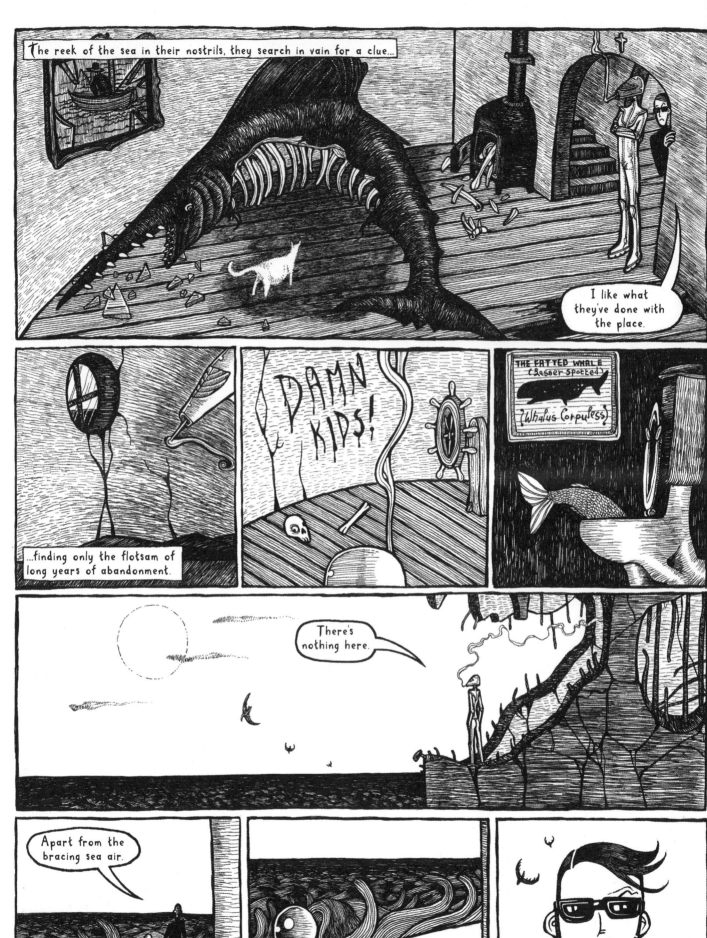

The reek of the sea in their nostrils, they search in vain for a clue...

I like what they've done with the place.

...finding only the flotsam of long years of abandonment.

DAMN KIDS!

THE FATTED WHALE (Lesser spotted) (Whalus Corpuless)

There's nothing here.

Apart from the bracing sea air.

And...?

What's this?

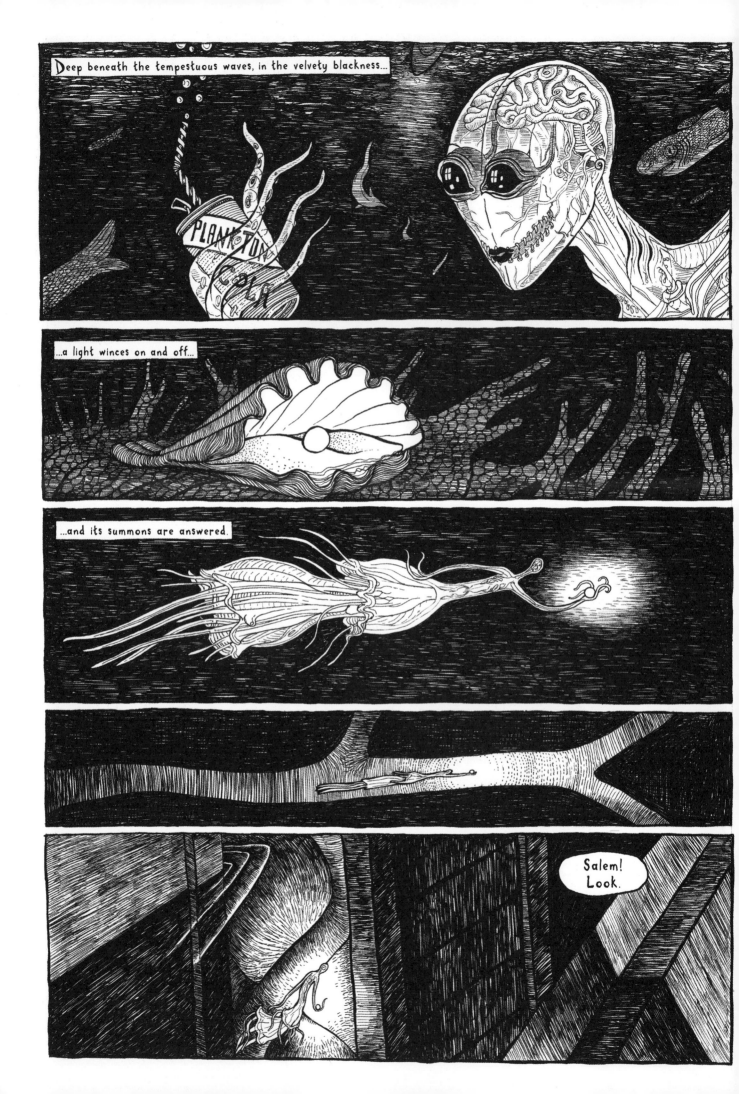

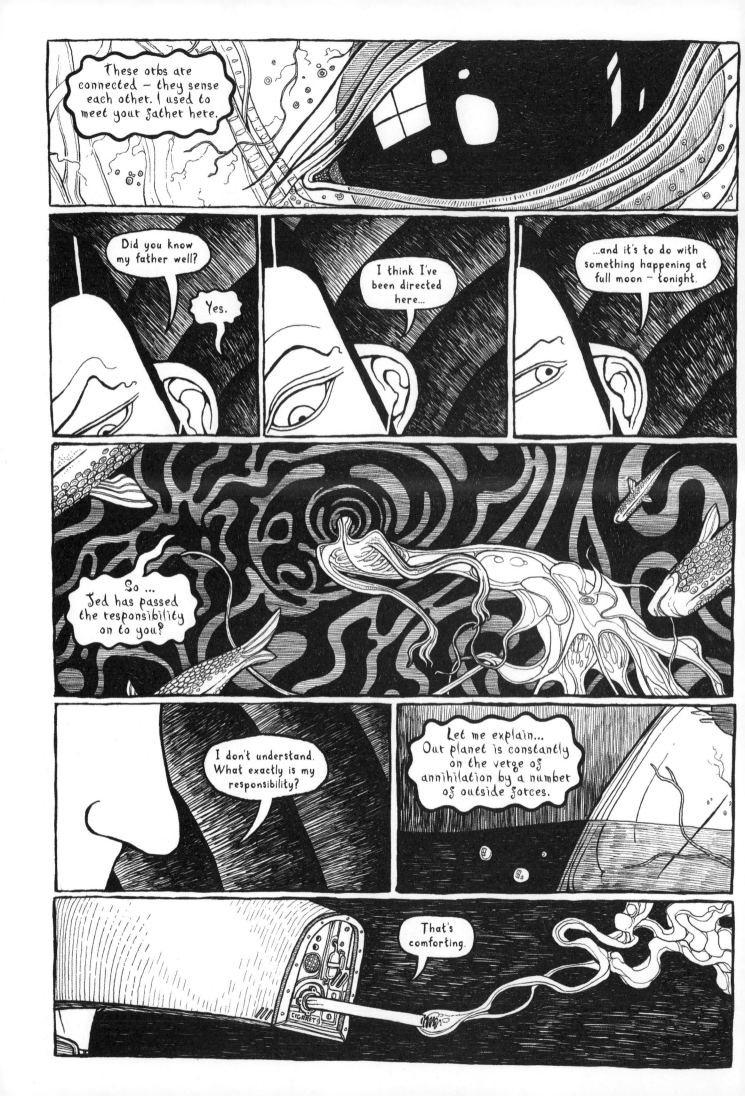

There ate seven of us who possess the orbs and ate able to awaken out ethetic doubles. Every seven yeats we have to take out places in the watchtowets ot out defences against these threats ate comptomised.

What are the watchtowers?

There ate many diffetent stories about how they came to be; what we know fot cettain is that they ate a kind of fottification atound out teality as we know it.

So how will I find my watchtower?

The familiat that inhabits yout orb will take you thete tonight.

You mean Oosik?

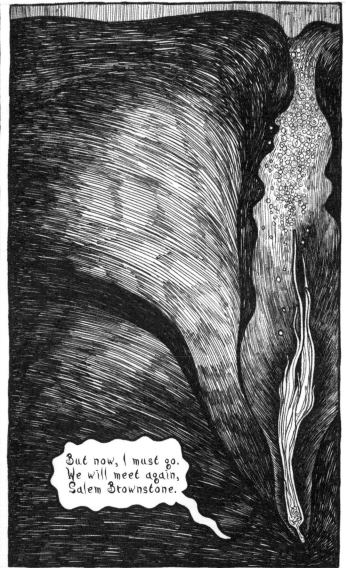

But now, I must go. We will meet again, Salem Brownstone.

I didn't like her — she seemed...

Slippery.

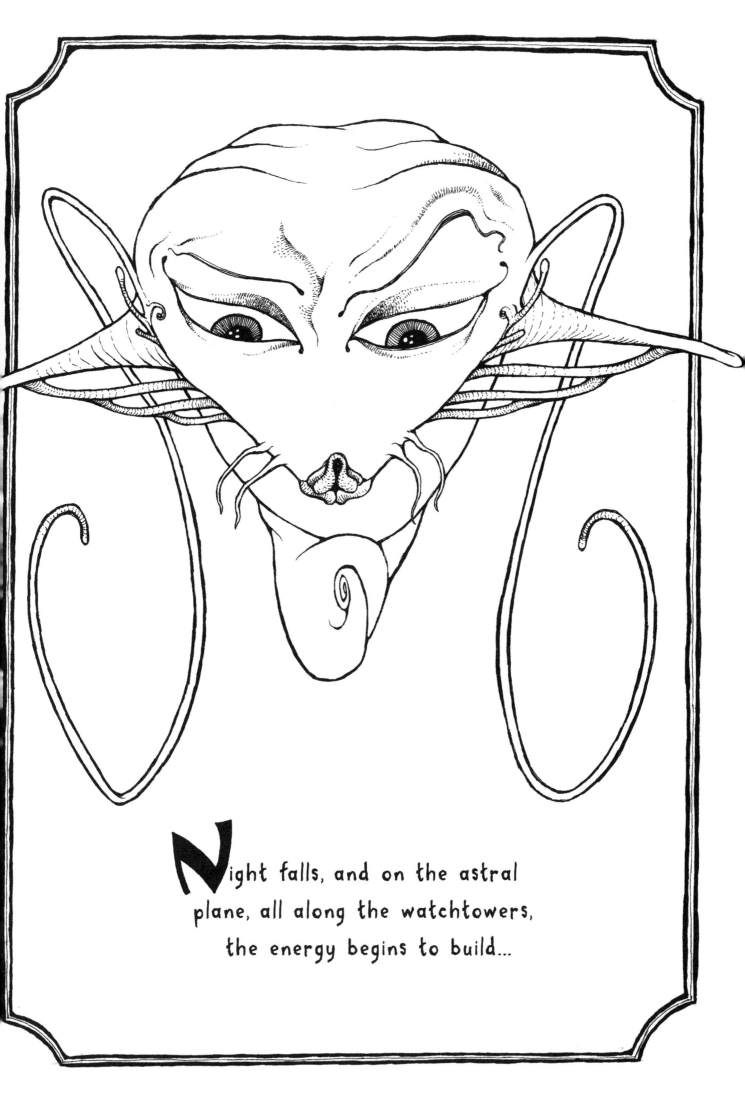

Night falls, and on the astral
plane, all along the watchtowers,
the energy begins to build...

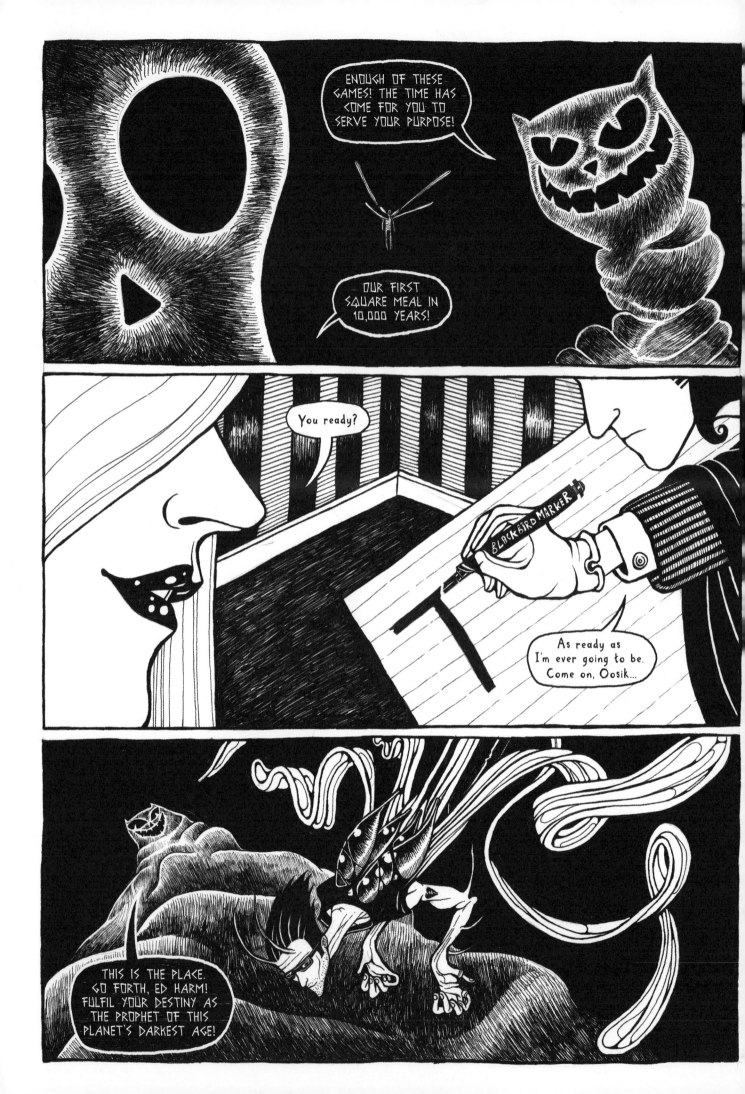

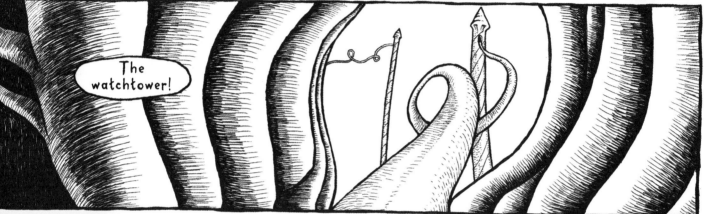

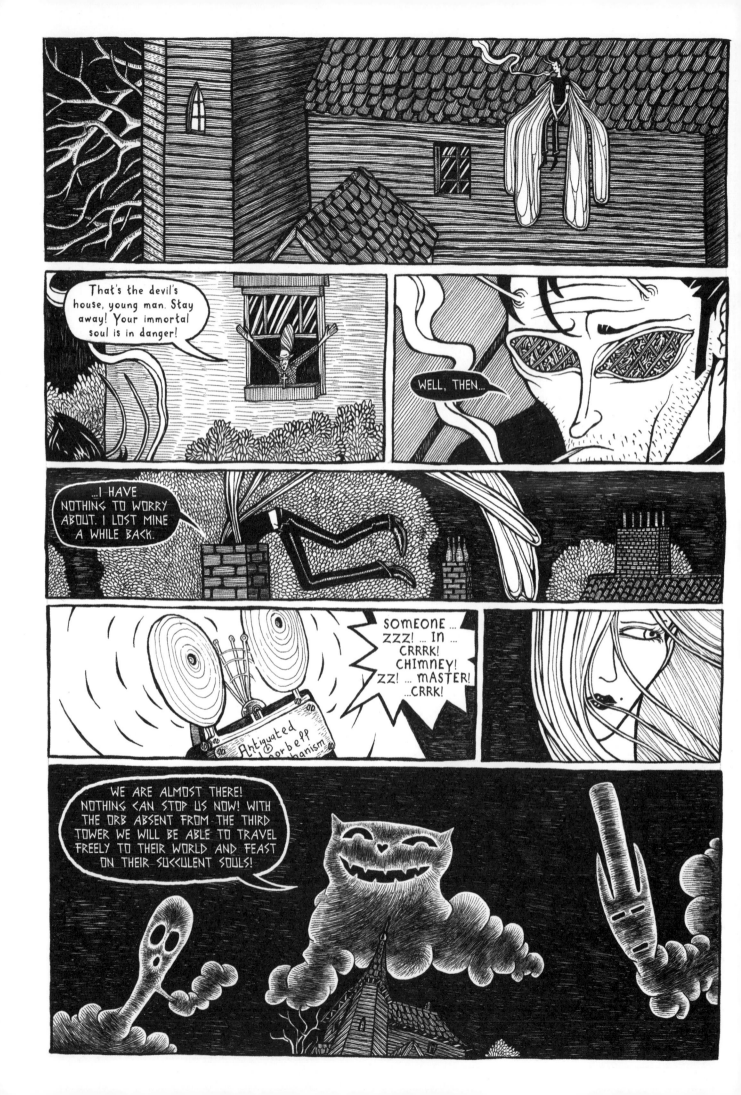

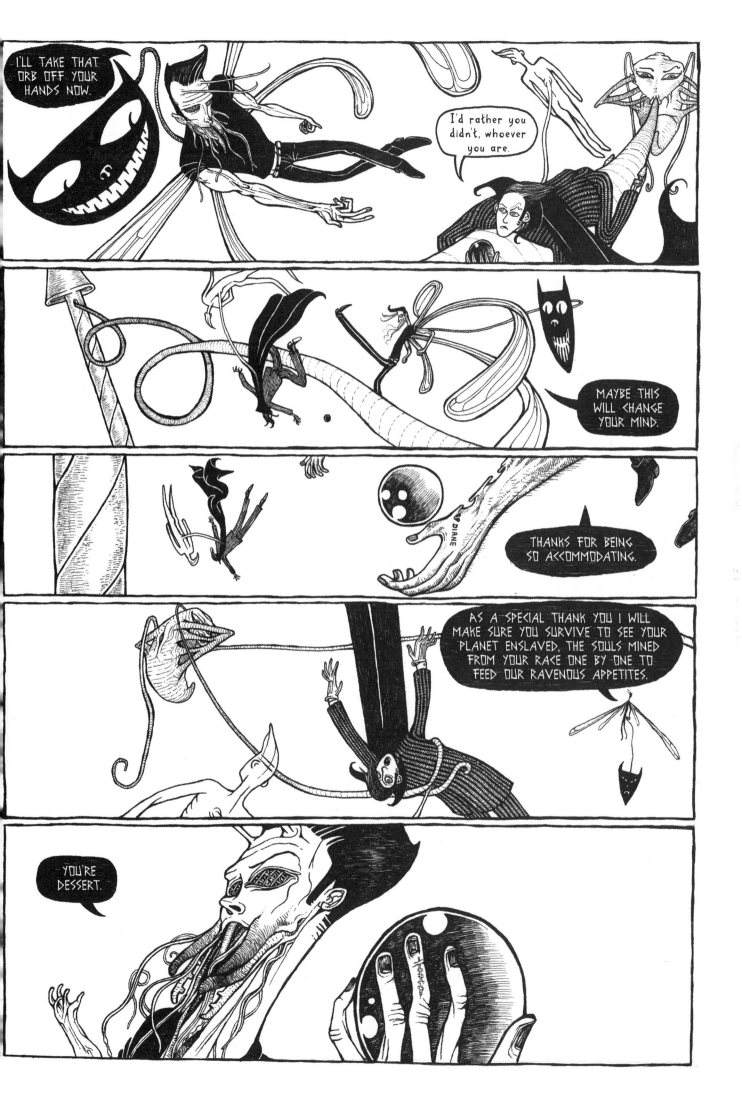

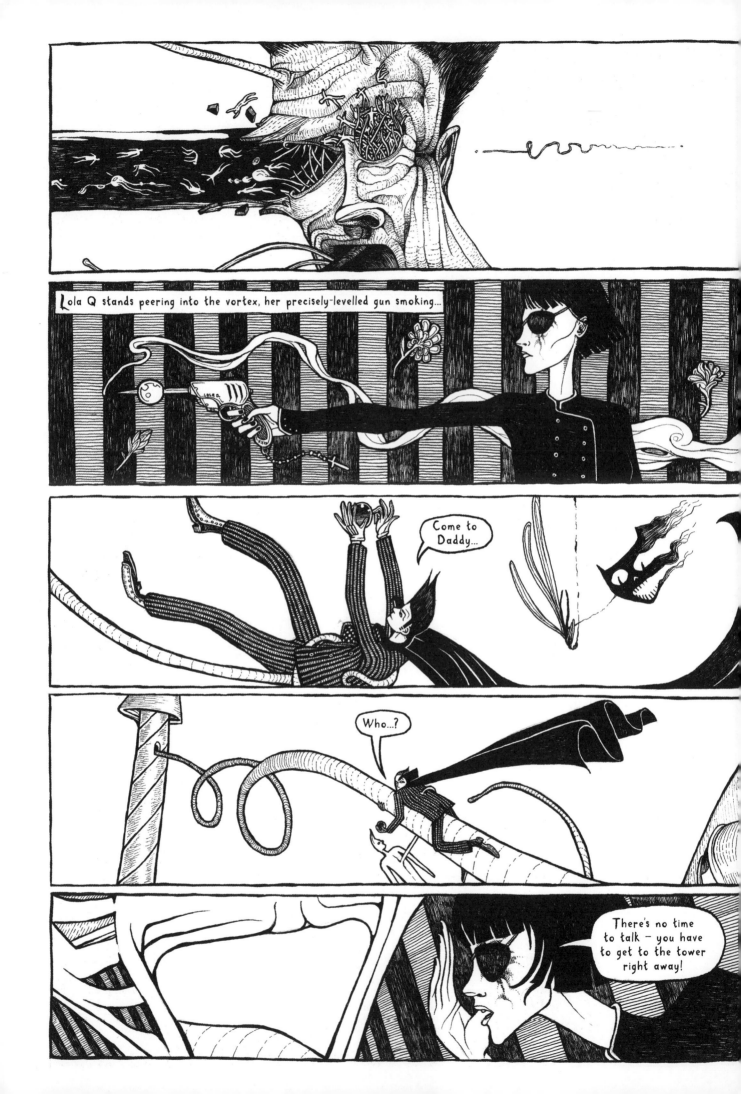

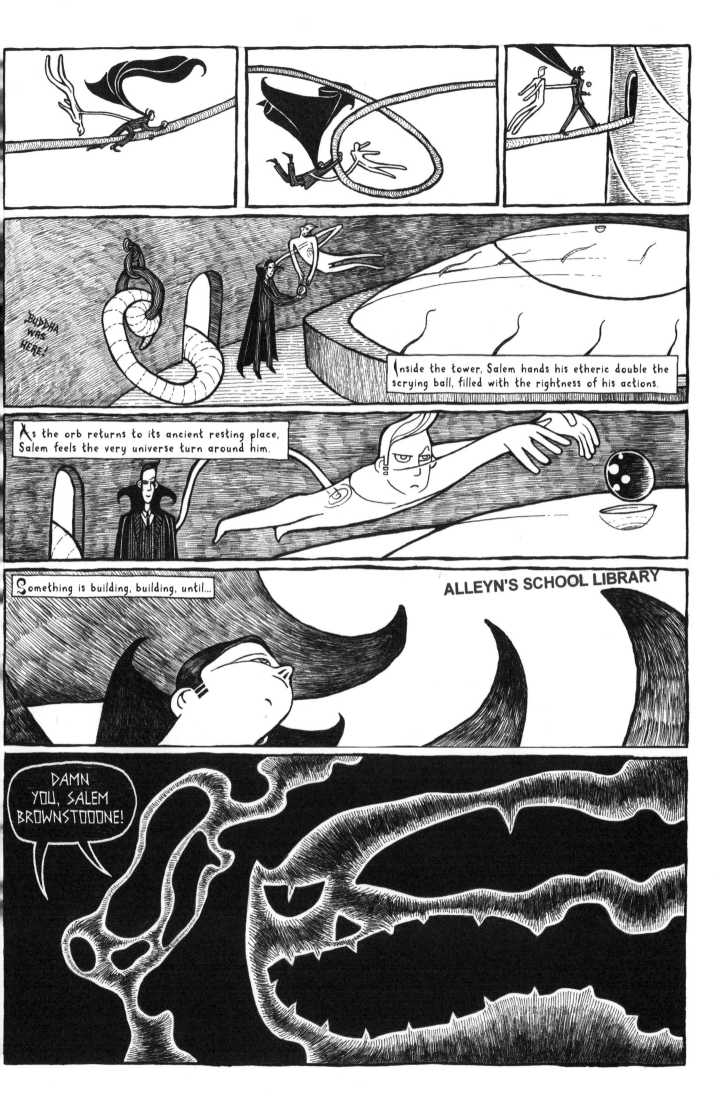

THE DARK ELDERS OF MU'BRIC

COOKIE
HERERO

ED HARM

salem brownstone

would like to thank his uncle Paul Gravett, his godparents Simon Davis and Sylvia Farago, Jefferson Hack, Patrick Insole, Harmony Korine, Fiona McMorrough, Anthony Minghella, Jon Morgan, Mark Sinclair, Lizzie Spratt & Sarah Such.
Abracadabra!

✱   ✱   ✱

Photo by Matt Hass

john harris dunning

This book is dedicated to Peter Watson, for all your love and support.

I'd like to thank my parents Carol and Simon Dunning, my sister Georgia Morris, and the rest of my family. The encouragement of my friends has been invaluable, especially that of Craig Bregman, Alex De Campi, Christian De Sousa, Lisa Cohn, Roland Erasmus, Jo Hebouche, Richard James, Lara Lombaard, Sacha Mardou, Mark Pool & Rory Stead.

Big up to the Midwich Cuckoos: Dylan, Imogen and Abigail Morris, Esmé & Milo Davis, Lucas & Max Abelson, Silva De Sousa, Alexander, Daniel & Thomas Fives, Saffron, Hannah and Amina Hebouche, Fynn Oldreive, Milo & Hela Watson & Harvey Yeomans.

✱   ✱   ✱

John Harris Dunning was born in Zululand, South Africa. He now lives in Hampstead, London's most haunted suburb.

Visit: www.tibet-foundation.org

Photo by Carmen Williams

nikhil singh

Salem was drawn sporadically over a period of seven years. Consequently, I am obliged to thank a lot of people whose help and assistance was both vital and invaluable.

The first half drawn at the Daily Deli, 13 Brownlow, Cape Town.
The second half at 10 Kidderpore Gardens, Hampstead.

CAPE TOWN
Thanks to Melanie for being a guiding light and for showing me how to build the pyramid. Thanks to Angelika for the fireside freakouts — they helped! Thanks to Sinead for keeping me on track. Thanks to Bona for being a sibling. Thanks to Cass for the psychic hotline. Thanks to Elise for the mermaids. Thanks to Gareth for finding the frequency. Thanks to Len for defending humanity. And thanks to Jemstone for always grounding me in the universe.

HAMPSTEAD
Thanks to Pekka for unimaginable support and unshakeable faith in rock and roll. Thanks to Simon Psi the all-seeing eye. Thanks to Alain for popping a cap in Satan's Nazi ass. Thanks to Juan-Erh for the plot on the Orient Express. Thanks to my mom for being a good friend. Thanks to Talitha for the dreams in the doll's house. And special thanks to Carmen, Empress of the two White Cats, for keeping me alive in deep space, guarding the gate to fairyland and riding the wild white unicorns.

✱   ✱   ✱

Witchboy. Were-cat. High ranking member of the Venusian Secret Service. Nikhil left school at 16 and has undergone no formal draining at any institutes of higher burning. He currently lives in an ivory tower and is never coming back to your planet EVER AGAIN.

Visit his grave at www.nikhilsingh.com

This is a work of fiction. Names, characters, places and incidents are either the product of the
author's imagination or, if real, are used fictitiously. All statements, activities, stunts, descriptions,
information and material of any other kind contained herein are included for entertainment purposes
only and should not be relied on for accuracy or replicated as they may result in injury.

First published 2009 by Walker Books Ltd
87 Vauxhall Walk, London SE11 5HJ

This edition published 2011

2 4 6 8 10 9 7 5 3 1

Text © 2009 John Harris Dunning
Illustrations © 2009 Nikhil Singh

The right of John Harris Dunning and Nikhil Singh to be identified as author and illustrator of this work
respectively has been asserted by them in accordance with the Copyright, Designs and Patents Act 1988

This book has been typeset in Little Grog

Printed in China

All rights reserved. No part of this book may be reproduced, transmitted or stored in an
information retrieval system in any form or by any means, graphic, electronic or mechanical, including
photocopying, taping and recording, without prior written permission from the publisher.

British Library Cataloguing in Publication Data:
a catalogue record for this book is available from the British Library

ISBN 978-1-4063-3176-9

www.walker.co.uk